A Note to Parents and

DK READERS is a compelling reading
children. The programme is designed i   with
leading literacy experts, including Cliff Moon M.Ed., who
has spent many years as a teacher and teacher educator
specializing in reading. Cliff Moon has written more than
160 books for children and teachers. He is series editor to
Collins Big Cat.

Beautiful illustrations and superb full-colour photographs
combine with engaging, easy-to-read stories to offer a fresh
approach to each subject in the series. Each DK READER
is guaranteed to capture a child's interest while developing
his or her reading skills, general knowledge, and
love of reading.

The five levels of DK READERS are aimed at different
reading abilities, enabling you to choose the books that
are exactly right for your child:

Pre-level 1: Learning to read
Level 1: Beginning to read
Level 2: Beginning to read alone
Level 3: Reading alone
Level 4: Proficient readers

The "normal" age at which a child begins
to read can be anywhere from three to eight
years old. Adult participation through the
lower levels is very helpful for providing
encouragement, discussing storylines and
sounding out unfamiliar words.

No matter which level you
select, you can be sure that you
are helping your child learn to
read, then read to learn!

LONDON, NEW YORK, MUNICH,
MELBOURNE and DELHI

Written by Fiona Lock

Series Editor Deborah Lock
Project Art Editor Mary Sandberg
Production Editor Sean Daly
Production Erika Pepe
Jacket Designer Mary Sandberg

Reading Consultant
Cliff Moon, M.Ed.

Published in Great Britain by
Dorling Kindersley Limited
80 Strand, London WC2R ORL

Copyright © 2008 Dorling Kindersley Limited
A Penguin Company

2 4 6 8 10 9 7 5 3 1
DD448 - 1/08

A CIP catalogue record for this book
is available from the British Library

ISBN: 978-1-40533-282-8

Colour reproduction by Colourscan, Singapore
Printed and bound in China by L Rex Printing Co., Ltd.

The publisher would like to thank the following for their kind
permission to reproduce their photographs:
a=above; b=below; c=centre; l=left; r=right; t=top

Alamy Images: Sally and Richard Greenhill 7tr; Picture Partners
4-5, 30-31; Trevor Smith 14-15. **Corbis:** Paul Barton / Zefa 10-11;
Heide Benser / Zefa 22-23; Alberto Biscaro 6-7; Jim Craigmyle 28-29;
Richard Cummins 17tr; Rick Gayle 13br, 13fbr; Paul Hardy 7bl; Dave
G. Houser 24fbl; Richard Hutchings 9tr; JLP / Sylvia Torres / Zefa
29tr; Moodboard 20-21; Touhig Sion / Corbis Sygma 16-17; Ariel
Skelley 21tr; Lee Snider / Photo Images 25tr; Tim Thompson 14tl.
DK Images: The American Museum of Natural History 18br, 18fbr,
18-19, 32bl; Robert L. Braun – modelmaker 17fbl; Jane Bull 10fbr,
11br; Graham High at Centaur Studios – modelmaker 16fbr, 32tl;
NASA 28br, 29fbr; NASA / Finley Holiday Films 29fbl; National
Railway Museum, New Delhi 24bc; Natural History Museum, London
16fbl, 17br, 17fbr, 19br; Stephen Oliver 9bl, 9fbl, 10fbl, 11bl, 30fbl;
Royal Tyrrell Museum of Palaeontology, Alberta, Canada 18c;
Senckenberg, Forschungsinstitut und Naturmuseum, Frankfurt. 19fbr;
Washington Park and Zoo Railway, Portland, Oregon 25bc; Jerry
Young 21br. **Getty Images:** Iconica / Blue Line Pictures 8-9; Stone /
Richard Elliott 26-27. **NASA:** 26br, 27bl, 27br, 32clb. **Science Photo
Library:** Indian Space Research Organisation 26fbr; MSFC / NASA
26fbl; Starsem 27bc. **Shutterstock:** Bianda Ahmad Hisham 14bl,
32cla; Alex Melnick 12-13.
Jacket images: *Front:* **Corbis:** Steve Kaufman bc; Tom & Dee Ann
McCarthy cla. **DK Images:** The American Museum of Natural
History cl. **Shutterstock:** Albert Campbell ftl.
All other images © Dorling Kindersley
For more information see: www.dkimages.com

Discover more at
www.dk.com

Contents

DK READERS

LEARNING TO READ pre-level 1

Family
Holiday

A Dorling Kindersley Book

We went on holiday for a week.

We packed our bags.

suitcase

We went on
an aeroplane.
We stayed in a hotel.

hotel

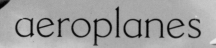

aeroplanes

swimming pool

On Monday,
we went to the beach.
We made
a big sandcastle.

sandcastle

  beach

bucket

We splashed in the sea and then ate ice cream.

ice cream

waves

fun fair

On Tuesday,
we went to a fun fair.
We went on some rides.

parade

We watched a parade.
There were lots of floats.

float

On Wednesday,
we went to see dinosaurs.

dinosaurs

teeth

We looked at
the skeletons.
Some were big and
some were small.

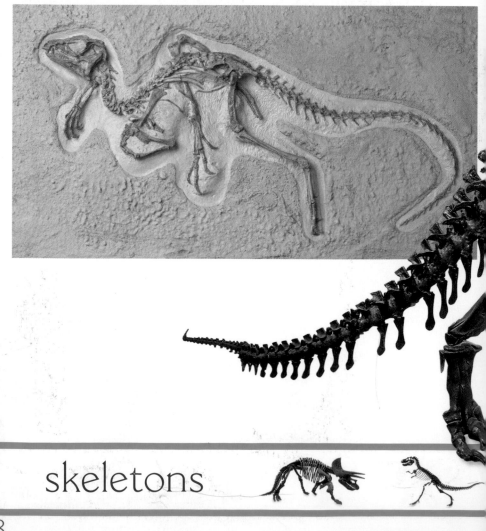

skeletons

skull

On Thursday, we went for a walk. We looked for insects.

net

insects

caterpillar

21

picnic basket

picnic

We had a picnic
in the park.

On Friday,
we rode on a train.
We went up
a steep mountain.

 trains

track

On Saturday, we looked at rockets at a space centre.

rockets

nose cone

We learnt about
the planets and
the stars.

planets

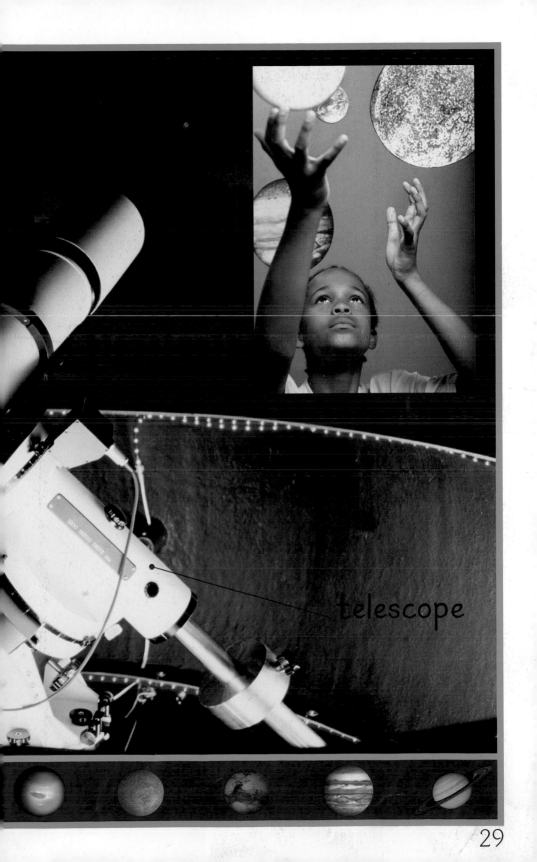

telescope

On Sunday,
we went home.
We looked at the photos
of our holiday.

photo

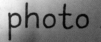

What do you like

o do on holiday?

Glossary

 **Dinosaur** a reptile that lived on Earth millions of years ago

 **Float** a decorated vehicle used in a parade

 **Planet** a large ball of rock or gas that moves around the sun

 **Rocket** a machine that flies into space

 **Skeleton** a strong framework of bones that supports the body